GR
BRI

This I-SPY book belongs to: _____

Introduction

All of us care about the environment. We want to protect the air and water from being poisoned by our waste. We need to prevent the habitats of plants and animals from being poisoned by our waste. We need to protect the habitats of plants and animals. It is necessary to use our precious natural resources carefully, trying not to waste them, so that there will be enough for our children and their children.

This concern is not new. Some Ancient Greek and Roman writers warned of the damage careless farming was doing to the land. In 1306 a law was passed to forbid the burning of coal in London, because of the pollution it caused. And a law of 1543 made it an offence to remove the roots of all the trees in a wood. Damage became more serious when factories were built producing more and more goods, often taking no account of how waste was disposed. Today we have learned to be more careful, in our homes as well as in factories.

The environment is all around us. Many examples can be seen of the harm done in the past and measures being taken to protect the environment. Many new products can now be recycled and are made from fewer or more renewable resources.

CAUTION: In this I-Spy book, we have included places such as recycling centres and landfill sites. These are potentially very dangerous and you should never enter such sites alone.

How to use your I-SPY book

As you work through this book, you will notice that the subjects are arranged in groups which are related to the kinds of places where you are likely to find things. You need 1000 points to send off for your I-Spy certificate (see page 64) but that is not too difficult because there are masses of points in every book. As you make each I-Spy, write your score in the box and, where there is a question, double your score if you can answer it. Check your answer against the correct one on page 63.

I-SPY TITLES AVAILABLE:

I-SPY points: 10

Date: _____

TRAMS

Some cities, such as Manchester have re-introduced trams as part of their transport solutions. They are quiet, cause less pollution, and can carry large numbers of passengers. They run on rails which are expensive to lay, so it is a large investment for most towns when considering alternative forms of transport.

BENDY-BUS

Bendy or articulated buses can be up to 18 metres long and can carry 120 passengers. They are often used at airports to move large numbers of people to and from the terminals.

I-SPY points: 10

Date: _____

LPG CAR

LPG stands for Liquefied Petroleum Gas, also known as Autogas. It's a lot cheaper than conventional fuels and produces much less pollution. There are an estimated 50,000 LPG vehicles on our roads. LPG requires special fuel tanks.

I-SPY points: 15

Date: _____

MICRO CAR

There are a number of micro cars available, such as the Smart car in the picture. They are all very economical with some diesel models giving over 80mpg (28km/l).

I-SPY points: 10

Date: _____

ELECTRIC CARS

Improvements in battery technology means that electric cars are becoming a real option. The latest type use L-ion (Lithium Ion) batteries giving them a top speed of 50mph (80km/h) and a range of 75 miles (120km) between charges that can take as little as 1 hour. This range will improve as battery technology progresses.

I-SPY points: 15

Date: _____

HYBRID CAR

Several manufacturers now have hybrids in their fleet; in slow traffic they run on batteries but out of town they have a conventional engine. They are much quieter vehicles and much better for the environment.

I-SPY points: 15

Date: _____

I-SPY points: 10
Double with answer

Date: _____

MODERN DIESEL CARS

Modern diesel engines can be up to 40% more efficient than petrol engines resulting in lower fuel consumption.

How did the diesel car get its name?

ELECTRIC BICYCLE

Battery powered bicycles are becoming popular for people who live and work in cities. The best can have a range of 60 miles and reach the legal limit of 24km/h (15mph). When the battery runs out – start pedalling!

I-SPY points: 15

Date: _____

TRAINS

Trains are considered green as they can carry lots of people! Some are capable of running on biofuel and others actually return electricity to the national grid when braking.

I-SPY points: 5

Date: _____

BIODIESEL

This is a growing technology that can be made from soya beans, sunflowers, oilseed rape or even algae. Double points for spotting a growing crop!

I-SPY points: 15

Date: _____

DID YOU KNOW that

tyres can help the environment?

The efficiency of a tyre – in other words, the amount of energy needed to move the tyre – can be improved by changing the way in which the tyre is made and by altering the patterns on the tyres, which reduces the noise the tyres make as they travel along the road.

Back in 1947, Michelin created what is now the standard for all tyres – the radial tyre.
Not only was this patented design more fuel-efficient, but the tyres were able to do many more miles before needing to be replaced.

In 1992 Michelin introduced a new GREEN tyre that was called the Michelin ENERGY and was made using new materials that resulted in lower fuel consumption, enhanced grip and longer tyre life.
Since then, these advances have resulted in a saving of over 9 billion litres of fuel and 23 million tonnes less CO_2 entering the atmosphere!

Michelin continues to develop tyres which help their customers to save costs and also minimise damage to the environment.
We re-groove and re-tread truck tyres to make them last longer.
We have also reduced the weight of our tyres – this is

very important because when a vehicle is lighter, it uses less fuel. This is especially important on planes.

Not many people know that Michelin also produces tractor tyres which are specially made to reduce damage to soil so that farmers can produce more food per acre.

At the end of their life tyres can be put to many uses. Shredded rubber is sometimes used in the construction of playgrounds, sports grounds and road surfaces. It is even used as 'chip mulch' in gardens to keep weeds from growing. Old tyres are also used as a fuel to heat cement kilns, where their high calorific value is excellent for producing the extreme temperatures required to make cement.

At Michelin, we have great respect for the planet. We see it as a moral obligation to recycle our tyres – and we are always looking for new ways to do this.

We also try to reduce our effect on the environment. For example, at our Dundee factory, we have installed two wind turbines which produce some of the electricity needed to power the plant.

In 1889, the Michelin brothers began a company that would develop and grow through innovation. Over a hundred years later, Michelin continues on this path to ensure that we meet the demands of tomorrow, today.

DRAUGHT SNAKE

Many house are today double glazed, sealing out draughts, but in older houses, doors don't fit so well allowing draughts to come in. A draught snake is the ideal thing to seal it up!

I-SPY points: 10

Date: _____

TURN THE LIGHTS OFF

Leaving lights on all over the house is a waste of resources and costs money. Please turn them off as you leave the room!

I-SPY points: 5

Date: _____

DRAW THE CURTAINS

A lot of heat can be lost through windows, especially old wooden or metal framed ones. Pulling the curtains provides extra insulation.

I-SPY points: 5

Date: _____

TURN IT OFF

Household appliances use electricity even when they are on standby. When possible turn them off at the wall switch, particularly overnight.

I-SPY points: 5

Date: _____

WHEELIE BIN

Some councils provide coloured wheelie bins for people to use for their recycling. The material is sorted later at the recycling centre.

I-SPY points: 5

Date: _____

PAPER SHREDDER

A great way to recycle junk mail and at the same time make free bedding for your hamster! Or you could put it on the compost heap to rot down into valuable compost.

I-SPY points: 10

Date: _____

I-SPY points: 10

Date: _____

ENERGY-RATED APPLIANCE

Most modern electrical appliances are rated for their efficiency in grades from A-G, with A being the best you can buy.

See if your equipment has green credentials.

I-SPY points: 15

Date: _____

LOFT INSULATION

A house can lose as much as 25% of its heat through its roof as warm air rises. Insulating the loft with a 300mm layer of densely packed fibre greatly reduces this loss. An insulated house costs less to heat.

DOUBLE GLAZING

It is more difficult for heat to escape through a window if the window is made with two panes of glass separated by a space filled with air. This is double glazing. It saves energy and also shuts out noise, making the house quieter. In very cold countries triple glazing is used.

I-SPY points: 5

Date: _____

ORGANIC VEGETABLE BOX SCHEME

These are becoming common. You can have a selection of fresh, in-season vegetables and fruit delivered straight to your house from a delivery van.

I-SPY points: 15

Date:

MOTION SENSOR LIGHTING

These devices help to cut down the electricity bill. The lights are only turned on when a persons movement activates them. They are often used for external security lighting.

I-SPY points: 10

Date:

TURN THE HEATING DOWN

A significant amount of energy can be saved just by turning the thermostat down one degree.

I-SPY points: 10

Date:

LOW ENERGY LIGHT BULBS

These have improved in recent years but can still take a while to 'warm up' but they are cheap to buy, last for years and help reduce the electricity bill.

I-SPY points: 5

Date: _____

CAVITY WALL INSULATION

This insulating substance is placed between the external walls of a house. It reduces the amount of heat that would otherwise escape.

I-SPY points: 15

Date: _____

DRAUGHT PROOFING

Draughts are caused by cold air blowing in through gaps around doors, windows, and letter boxes. Strips of draught-proofing material can seal these gaps, making the house more comfort able and reducing heating bills.

I-SPY points: 15

Date: _____

RECYCLING BOX

Many houses are now responsible for sorting their rubbish into specially provided recycling boxes which are collected from the roadside.

I-SPY points: 5

Date:

RECYCLING CENTRE

With the separate containers for the different materials.

I-SPY points: 15

Date:

INFORMATION

Information sheets on recycling are now available at centres.

I-SPY points: 10

Date:

BATTERY RECYCLE

Don't throw away old, flat batteries as they contain hazardous and valuable materials that can be reclaimed via your local recycling centre.

I-SPY points: 15

Date: _____

PLASTIC CONTAINER BANK

Most plastics can be recycled. They are made into new products, such as soft-drink bottles, packaging, and bags for life. Plastic banks have pictures telling you which articles can be recycled.

I-SPY points: 10

Date: _____

TYRE RE-USE

Worn out tyres can be used in a variety of ways. Chopped up they make safe playground covering that is child friendly. Around race tracks they can provide safety for racing drivers and on farms they are used to weigh down tarpaulins.

I-SPY points: 15

Date: _____

FRIDGE AND FREEZERS

Old fridges and freezers must be disposed of properly as they can contain dangerous CFC gasses. If this gas leaks, it depletes the ozone layer which protects the earth from being overheated by the sun. Never climb into a fridge or freezer at any time as they can be very dangerous.

I-SPY points: 15

Date:

MOBILE PHONES

Mobile telephones rarely wear out, most just go out of fashion. In which case they can be donated to Third World users or the materials they are made of can be recovered and reused.

I-SPY points: 15

Date:

GLASS

Old glass can be crushed, melted, and mixed to make new glass. This saves energy and reduces the amount of glass going to waste and ultimately in our landfill.

I-SPY points: 10

Date:

PAPER

Paper is made from pulped wood, the pulping process uses a lot of energy. Old paper can be re pulped and used to make recycled paper. This saves energy and stops waste paper being buried in landfill sites and saves a few trees.

I-SPY points: 10

Date: _____

WASTE OIL

When a car is serviced, its engine oil is changed. Garages collect this oil and send it to a reprocessing plant where it's cleaned and recycled. The oil from cars serviced at home can be taken to an oil bank.

I-SPY points: 15

Date: _____

TEXTILES

Clean old clothes and shoes are collected at special banks in recycling centres. This saves materials and reduces the amount of waste in landfill sites.

I-SPY points: 15

Date: _____

LANDFILL

Whatever you have leftover that can't be reclaimed, recycled or reused will unfortunately have to go in your rubbish bin. It will either end up in a land-fill site to rot or be burned in an incinerator.

I-SPY points: 15

Date: _____

CARDBOARD

Cardboard is a valuable commodity that can be recycled to make more cardboard!

I-SPY points: 10

Date: _____

TV'S AND MONITORS

Most parts of a TV or computer monitor can be reclaimed and reused.

I-SPY points: 10

Date: _____

LIGHTBULBS

Even energy saving light bulbs should be recycled.

I-SPY points: 20

Date: _____

GREEN WASTE

Recycling centres will take all your garden waste and cuttings. It will rot down and form compost.

I-SPY points: 10

Date: _____

METAL

Recycling metal is an easy way to re-use the materials again to make new items.

I-SPY points: 15

Date: _____

WOOD AND TIMBER

Any old wooden objects or off-cuts of wood can be recycled. Some furniture can be given to charity shops.

I-SPY points: 10

Date:

AEROSOLS

Never play with discarded aerosols, the gasses and containers can be dangerous.

I-SPY points: 15

Date:

CHARITY SHOPS

What a great way to obtain stylish clothes, shoes and books at a fraction of the normal high street price. It can be fun hunting down a bargain too!

I-SPY points: 5

Date:

SPREADING MANURE ON FIELDS

Farmers use immense quantities of straw for winter animal bedding. Mixed with animal waste and spread by machine it improves soil fertility and saves buying expensive artificial fertiliser.

I-SPY points: 10

Date: _____

BIRD BOXES

Give the birds desirable residences and they will stay to snack on the insect pests and weed seeds in your garden. You can buy boxes or even make your own.

I-SPY points: 15

Date: _____

HORTICULTURAL FLEECE

This is a lightweight woven fabric used by gardeners to warm up the ground prior to spring planting. It can also be used as a cover to protect tender plants from frost damage.

I-SPY points: 15

Date: _____

SUNFLOWERS

A summer garden is incomplete without a row of tall, bright yellow sunflowers nodding in the summer breeze. Some of the giants can reach 4 metres (13ft) high. You could grow one in a pot.

I-SPY points: 10

Date: _____

BAT BOXES

Bats need small holes in walls to climb to the places where they roost. Modern buildings have no suitable holes so a bat box fixed on a wall or tree is an ideal alternative. If bats use the box, you may see them flying from it at dusk.

I-SPY points: 25

Date: _____

ANTI-WEED MEMBRANE

Also known as geotextiles, these synthetic water and air permeable membranes will provide excellent long-term weed control but they do need to be pegged or weighted down.

I-SPY points: 15

Date: _____

COMPOST TUMBLER

Put the garden waste and kitchen peelings into the drum, turn it every couple of days and in a few weeks you should have wonderful rich compost.

I-SPY points: 20

Date: _____

COMPOST HEAP OR BIN

Grass cuttings, weeds, old pet bedding and non-woody plant material (but not waste food) can be recycled via a compost heap. It will turn into a dark, sweet-smelling substance that can be spread on the soil to improve it. Most serious gardeners have a compost heap.

I-SPY points: 10

Date: _____

GARDEN POND

One of the best things a gardener can do is to dig a pond. Many birds and insects will benefit from a pond and help the garden grow.

I-SPY points: 10

Date: _____

PROVIDE A BIRD BATH

If you can't provide a pond then a bird-bath is the next best thing. If possible site it near to some bushes for the birds to preen in and hide from predators.

I-SPY points: 15

Date: _____

ERECT A BIRD TABLE

If you have a garden you may put out food to attract wild birds. The food should be placed on a bird table out of the reach of cats and it's best to use the kind of food the birds eat naturally. Did you know that bread has very little nutritional value to birds?

I-SPY points: 10

Date: _____

PLANT A TREE

Or better still plant 10! If you have the space plant trees for the wildlife of the future. Small trees, called whips are not expensive but don't forget to provide a spiral tree guard to help them grow.

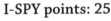 I-SPY points: 25

Date: _____

PEANUT FEEDER

Feeding wild birds helps them survive in bad weather. It also holds them in your area ready to eat insect pests in your vegetable patch or borders. Don't forget the water too!

I-SPY points: 15

Date: _____

WORM FARM

If you like to grow your own flowers and vegetables, harness the power of the worms! From a small self-contained farm they will make the finest soil conditioner called vermicompost. The worms will eat all your kitchen waste, some dead leaves and a few grass clippings.

I-SPY points: 20

Date: _____

WATER BUTT

You can use the pure rainwater that collects in your water butt to grow vegetables and flowers from seed. If you leave the top slightly open the birds can have a drink too but be careful, water butts can be dangerous to small children.

I-SPY points: 10

Date: _____

LICHENS

Most lichens are killed by sulphur, so if you see them growing on trees, walls, and rocks you can be fairly certain the air does not contain sulphur dioxide. Sulphur dioxide is one of the substances that causes acid rain.

What is a lichen?

I-SPY points: 15

Double with answer

Date: _____

POLYTUNNEL

More and more people are realising the benefits even a small polytunnel can bring to a garden. Not only will your plants be protected from the worst weather but you can also extend the growing season by several months giving you fresh, healthy vegetables and fruit for longer.

I-SPY points: 20

Date: _____

The companies and organisations listed in this Conservation section all work really hard to promote their causes. Most of them are well known names – gain points for I-Spying their work.

PTES – PEOPLE'S TRUST FOR ENDANGERED SPECIES

people's trust for
endangered species

I-SPY points: 20

Date: _____

PTES have been conserving endangered species for over 30 years. They have a special focus on British mammals, and run several nationwide public surveys to help monitor a range of native species such as hedgehogs, stag beetles and dormice. Each year they offer an exciting range of Wildlife Encounters so that their supporters and the general public can see wildlife up close and learn from the conservationists and scientists.

MSC – MARINE STEWARDSHIP COUNCIL

The MSC's fishery certification program and seafood ecolabel recognises and rewards sustainable fishing. They are a global organisation working with fisheries, scientists, conservation groups and the public to promote the best environmental practise for our food which comes from the sea.

I-SPY points: 20

Date: _____

THE WILDLIFE TRUST

There are 47 local Wildlife Trusts across the UK, the Isle of Man & Alderney, with over 791,000 members and 2,250 nature reserves. These local wildlife conservation charities protect all habitats and species. From wildflowers to ancient woodlands, marine wildlife to windswept moorlands, their aim is to create a wildlife-rich landscape for everyone to enjoy and treasure. Why not check out their award-winning website for children and families: www.wildlifewatch.org.uk where you can also find out about how to join and support them.

I-SPY points: 20

Date: _____

RENT A CHRISTMAS TREE

Have a living tree delivered right to your front door just for the Christmas period. After the holiday it will be collected and returned to its field to help combat carbon dioxide emissions, thus helping the environment.

I-SPY points: 25

Date: _____

CPRE – CAMPAIGN FOR THE PROTECTION OF RURAL ENGLAND

Campaign to Protect Rural England

CPRE aims to look after the countryside with its beautiful landscapes and villages and the freedom and enjoyment it offers us all. They do this by carefully planning where new development happens, encouraging people not to drop litter and by protecting land through 'Green Belts', 'National Parks' and 'Areas of Outstanding Natural Beauty'. They have helped protect many of the special features you can spot in the countryside: ancient hedgerows, dry stone walls, red telephone boxes and small village shops. You may even hear birdsong or a running stream while you are exploring, which could mean you are in one of CPRE's tranquil areas.

I-SPY points: 20

Date: _____

FSC – FOREST STEWARDSHIP COUNCIL

FSC is an international, non-governmental organisation dedicated to promoting responsible management of the world's forests. It was founded in 1993 in response to public concern about deforestation and demand for a trustworthy wood labelling scheme.

I-SPY points: 20

Date: _____

RSPB – ROYAL SOCIETY FOR THE PROTECTION OF BIRDS

The conservation charity's work is driven by a passionate belief that we all have a responsibility to protect birds, other wildlife and the environment.

The RSPB has over a million members, including nearly 170,000 youth members. Its 200 nature reserves covering almost 130,000 hectares are home to 80% of our rarest or most threatened bird species and offer wonderful days out for the whole family. Whether you want some serious birdwatching or a nice stroll followed by tea and cake there is an RSPB reserve to explore close to you. www.rspb.org.uk

I-SPY points: 25

Date: _____

THE BUMBLEBEE CONSERVATION TRUST

Bumblebees are beautiful, hard working and incredibly important pollinators. The UK had 27 species, but sadly 3 are nationally extinct, and others are seriously threatened. Everyone can help save the sound of summer! Our gardens cover more than 1million hectares, far exceeding the combined area of all nature reserves. Many are populated with exotic flowers that produce little or no pollen and nectar and are not bumblebee friendly.

Why not try growing traditional cottage garden flowers and native wildflowers?

I-SPY points: 25

Date:

KEEP BRITAIN TIDY

More than two million pieces of litter are dropped in the UK every day which costs over £780 million a year to clean. Please ensure that you and your family dispose of your litter in the correct place.

I-SPY points: 20

Date:

WOODLAND TRUST

Established in 1972 and the UK's leading woodland conservation charity. Over the last 30 years they have acquired more than 1,000 woodland sites covering over 20,000 hectares (50,000 acres). They also have over 300,000 members and supporters who help continue their work.

I-SPY points: 25

Date: _____

BLUE FLAG BEACHES

Blue Flag is a prestigious, international award scheme that acts as a guarantee to tourists that the beach they are visiting is one of the best in the country. It is awarded to coastal destinations which have achieved the highest quality in water, facilities, safety, environmental education and management.

I-SPY points: 25

Date: _____

WIND TURBINE FARM

Electricity can be generated by large blades, like an aircraft propeller, that are mounted on tall towers and turned by the wind. A group of these generators is called a wind farm. The generators have to be widely separated, so wind farms occupy a large area.

I-SPY points: 20

Date: _____

MULCHES

A thick layer of woodchips called mulch is spread on the ground around trees, bushes and flowers beds. Light cannot penetrate the chips which stops weed seeds germinating. It looks quite smart and natural and reduces the use of pesticides.

I-SPY points: 10

Date: _____

35

SMOKELESS COAL OR COAL FIRE

Open fires are not as common as they used to be due to the increase of gas and oil central heating but in the countryside, you will easily see a plume of smoke rising from the chimney of a coal fire.

I-SPY points: 10

Date: _____

IRRIGATION

In the drier parts of the country, no crops would grow properly unless they were given water by an irrigation system, often from a high pressure spray pumped from a nearby river or tank.

I-SPY points: 10

Date: _____

Connecting **growers** to **people with land to share**

RIVER COTTAGE LANDSHARE

This is novel idea! An area of land too large to be managed by one family is shared and worked by several. Everybody works hard and shares the costs and the harvest.

I-SPY points: 25

Date: _____

WILLOW OR POPLAR COPPICE

Willow and Poplar trees grow very quickly and will re-grow after harvesting which is known as coppicing. The harvested wood can be pelletized and used to fuel power stations instead of coal.

I-SPY points: 15

Date: _____

ELEPHANT GRASS/ MISCANTHUS

This fast growing grass is very versatile. It too can be pelletized and used in power stations or chopped and used as animal bedding. It can also be converted into biofuel and used to power vehicles.

I-SPY points: 10

Date: _____

LOGS FOR FUEL

If you live outside a town it's likely that either you or one of your neighbours will have a wood burning stove or open fire.

I-SPY points: 5

Date: _____

TRADITIONAL WINDMILL

Once a common sight, windmills were dotted all over the country. Some were used to mill grain into flour but others were used to pump water, an early form of land reclamation by drainage; a clever use of wind power!

I-SPY points: 10

Date: _____

WATERWHEEL

Waterwheels have been widely used since the Middle Ages to power mills of various sorts including cotton, animal feed and flour. Now your best chance of seeing one will be at a Heritage Museum.

I-SPY points: 10

Date: _____

SOLAR POWERED ROAD SIGNS

These are most often used in rural areas where electricity is unavailable. They are especially common on stretches of road where speeding is a safety issue.

I-SPY points: 15

Date: _____

MARINE CURRENT TURBINE

These machines show great promise, generating electricity from the power of the tides without blocking the estuary to wildlife or shipping. Only one is currently installed in the UK in the mouth of Strangford Lough, Northern Ireland.

I-SPY points: 40

Date: _____

SEWAGE TREATMENT PLANT

Sewage used to be discharged directly into rivers or the sea causing major pollution incidents and killing fish. Now, at all sewage treatment plants, it is filtered and processed until the residue can be discharged without causing harm.

I-SPY points: 25

Date:

SOLAR PANELS

Solar panels are becoming more common in the UK and are usually on roofs. The panels are heated by the sun's rays and the heat generated is transferred into the house. In some parts of the country, solar panels can provide all the summer water-heating.

I-SPY points: 15

Date:

COOLING TOWERS

Electricity is a very clean form of energy. It is generated in power stations that usually have big cooling towers.

I-SPY points: 15

Date: _____

HYDRO ELECTRIC SCHEME

First a river is dammed to make a lake. The water can only escape through narrow tunnels in the dam wall which contain turbines. Gravity does all the work generating electricity by making the water spin the propeller-like turbines.

I-SPY points: 25

Date: _____

STAYCATION

Recently there has been a trend for lots of families to stay in Britain for their annual holiday. Why not? It's a beautiful place, especially in the nice warm weather.

I-SPY points: 15 for a family on the beach

Date: _____

FARMERS MARKETS

At these markets you can buy locally produced cheeses, organic fruit, vegetables, meat and so much more. It's also a great place to meet up with friends and relatives.

I-SPY points: 10

Date: _____

43

LOCAL SHOPS

We need to support local shops,
particularly in villages as they are
often the heart of a community.
Supermarkets are very convenient
but nothing beats "The Local
Shop" for capturing the
atmosphere of the region.

I-SPY points: 15

Date: _____

SCOUT POST

The Scout Movement collects local
postal deliveries at Christmas
time in some areas and hand
deliver your cards!

I-SPY points: 30

Date: _____

EUROPEAN ECO LABEL

The flower is the logo of the European Eco-label. It is a voluntary scheme designed to encourage businesses to market products and services that are kinder to the environment and for European consumers to easily identify them.

I-SPY points: 25

Date: _____

SOIL ASSOCIATION

The Soil Association organic symbol is the UK's largest and most recognisable trademark for organic produce – over 80% of organic products in Britain carry the mark. Wherever you see it you can be sure that the food you have purchased has been produced and processed to strict animal welfare and environmental standards.

I-SPY points: 25

Date: _____

CARDBOARD PACKAGING

Depending on its quality, recycled paper can be made into writing paper, envelopes, tissues, or egg cartons. Much of our brown wrapping paper, cardboard, and other packaging is made from recycled paper.

I-SPY points: 5

Date: _____

RECHARGEABLE BATTERIES

A very environmentally friendly way of storing and using electricity! Good quality rechargeable batteries can be re-used hundreds of times and can be re-cycled when they are eventually finished with.

I-SPY points: 5

Date: _____

LINE DRY NOT TUMBLE DRY

Don't waste expensive electricity by using a tumble drier. When possible hang washing out on a line or whirligig to get that wonderful fresh air smell.

I-SPY points: 10

Date: _____

FREE RANGE HENS

What a joy it is to collect freshly laid eggs from your own flock of hens. They will also help to keep your garden free of nasty bugs! But be sure to lock the hens away at night.

I-SPY points: 15

Date: _____

BUY UK PRODUCE

It's not good for the planet when we buy unseasonal foodstuff in winter from far away countries. Just think how much fuel was used by the aeroplane and trucks that bought them to you.

I-SPY points: 10

Date: _____

PUMP NOT AEROSOL

Before aerosol cans were invented, people used bottles with a small pump, worked by hand, that forced the contents through a nozzle. Now you can buy a bottle and refill it when it is empty.

I-SPY points: 10

Date: _____

FREECYCLE NETWORK

A great, free, internet based system to recycle most unwanted items. Toys that you no longer want, could be just what another child needs.

I-SPY points: 20

Date: _____

RECYCLE PRINTER CARTRIDGES

Re-manufactured ink cartridges are usually as good as the original item but because they are refilled, are cheaper.

I-SPY points: 20

Date: _____

MAIL PREFERENCE SERVICE

Cut down on waste paper by registering for a preference service and the amount of unwanted mail that arrives on your mat can be drastically reduced. This is a free service.

I-SPY points: 10

Date: _____

PAPER FREE BILLING

A great and green way of saving paper. Have your household utility bills delivered electronically to your computer and file them digitally if you need to keep a copy. Some suppliers give a discount for this method.

I-SPY points: 10

Date: _____

USE E-MAIL

Keep in touch with friends and relatives around the world using e-mail. You can even have a long distance conversation if you can type quickly.

I-SPY points: 5

Date: _____

NATURAL CLEANING SOLUTIONS

These cleaning solutions use plant extracts and mineral based ingredients that degrade naturally without leaving harmful residues on you, your clothes or the planet.

I-SPY points: 20

Date: _____

WASH AT 30° OR LESS

There are many products on the market that allow you to wash your clothes and reduce your energy bill by reducing the water temperature.

I-SPY points: 20

Date: _____

CYCLING

What a great way to travel! You get to see so much more from a bicycle since there is no engine to frighten wildlife. Your bike does not produce any emissions and needs no fuel!

I-SPY points: 15

Date: _____

WALKING

Another great form of exercise. Once again no engine, no fuel, no pollution. You can go when and where you like and with a little extra effort you can get right to the top of the hill to enjoy the view.

I-SPY points: 10

Date: _____

GET AN ALLOTMENT

Nothing tastes quite as good as your own freshly harvested and cooked vegetables. You also gain immense satisfaction from having raised your own food from seeds and defeated any pests along the way!

I-SPY points: 15

Date: _____

CLOTH BAGS FOR LIFE

These bags are often made from a renewable and sustainable plant resource called Jute. When processed it produces a vegetable fibre which can be woven and when finally discarded it totally decomposes putting valuable nutrients back into the soil. It is estimated that the jute industry supports 5 million people in the poorest regions on earth.

I-SPY points: 15

Date: _____

FAIR TRADE

The FAIRTRADE Mark gives a guarantee to consumers that producers in developing countries have been paid a fair and stable price so that they can provide for their families. Producers also receive an additional premium to invest in community projects of their choice such as clean water, healthcare and education. There are many products that carry the FAIRTRADE Mark from bananas and chocolate to cotton and flowers.

I-SPY points: 25

Date: _____

Personally Green

ORGANIC FOODS

By using methods such as "companion planting" and hand weeding it's perfectly possible to grow food that doesn't contain residues of chemicals so often used in intensive farming.

I-SPY points: 15

Date: _____

CITY PARK

Parks in towns provide open space for children to play and places where people can walk or rest among trees, flower beds, and lawns. Many of our parks were laid out in the last century and imitate natural countryside or the grounds around stately homes.

I-SPY points: 5

Date: _____

LOVE FOOD, HATE WASTE

About 8.3 million tonnes of food is thrown away by families every year! Most of that is perfectly good food that we 'over-bought' or forgot to use. Buy what you need and try to eat it!

LOVE FOOD hate waste

I-SPY points: 15

Date: _____

PARK AND RIDE

Many towns and cities encourage motorists to park on the outskirts of town and travel to the centre by bus. 'Park and ride' schemes reduce the amount of city-centre traffic, so buses and essential vehicles can move more freely. Less space is needed for car parks, too. Less slow moving traffic also means less air pollution.

I-SPY points: 10

Date: _____

CLEAR SKIES

Years ago, smoke from thousands of coal fires polluted the air over most industrial cities and the mixture of smoke and fog produced thick fogs called smog, causing major health problems. Today, chimneys are not allowed to belch black smoke and skies that were once usually overcast are now often clear.

I-SPY points: 10

Date: _____

CAR SCRAPYARD

Old and wrecked cars are taken to dumps where they lie in untidy heaps. After all usable parts have been removed, the cars are crushed into blocks of metal and sent to be melted down and the steel reused.

I-SPY points: 15

Date: _____

CLEAN BUILDINGS

The smoke that once made the air dirty also deposited black soot on buildings and statues. The pollutants were acidic and as well as blackening the stone, they dissolved it. Now the air is cleaner, the stonework can be cleaned, and city centres are being restored to the way they looked when they were first built.

What is the main ingredient in acid air pollution from coal-burning?

I-SPY points: 15
Double with answer

Date: _____

LITTER

Discarded litter blows around making the streets or countryside untidy. It's not good for animals that may eat it and looks unsightly. Once it has scattered, litter is difficult to collect. You should always use the litter bins in streets and lay-bys.

I-SPY points: 5

Date: _____

WASTE INCINERATION PLANT

Instead of burying waste, it can be burned to produce useful heat. The only way to dispose of some chemical and hospital wastes safely is to burn them at high temperatures. Waste is burned in incineration plants and sometimes the heat generated is reused.

I-SPY points: 15

Date: _____

SMOKEY VEHICLES

If a car is not serviced properly it can emit smoke from the exhaust. New air and oil filters plus an oil change will help the vehicle to not only run more efficiently but will also save money because it will use less fuel.

BELCHING CHIMNEYS

Smoke and many chemicals once poured out of old-fashioned, factory chimneys. Modern chimneys have a spiral vane on the outside to conduct heat away from the gasses inside. Harmful substances are collected and disposed of safely. New industries generally cause less pollution.

I-SPY points: 15

Date: _____

I-SPY points: 15

Date: _____

FLY TIPPING

Fly tipping is the name given to
the illegal dumping of rubbish. It
is sometimes done by commercial
contractors who wish to avoid
having to pay a charge for burying
it in a landfill site. It is a very
large and expensive problem for
local councils.

I-SPY points: 15

Date:

ABANDONED VEHICLES

Abandoned vehicles are often
the result of either joyriding or
the unwillingness of owners to
pay for the removal of unwanted
vehicles. They are not only an
eyesore but also a health hazard.

I-SPY points: 15

Date:

GRAFFITI

Defacing public buildings with paint, usually aerosols, is unsightly and costs thousands of pounds to remove.

I-SPY points: 5

Date: _____

CHEWING GUM

Chewing gum is amongst the most antisocial substance to be found on the pavements of our towns and cities. It is unsightly and extremely difficult and expensive to remove. Dispose of it in a bin.

I-SPY points: 5

Date: _____

MARINE POLLUTION

The practise of discharging waste water, contaminated with old oil and refuse into the open ocean is killing fish and other creatures and damaging beaches and marine habitats.

I-SPY points: 10

Date:

FLOTSAM AND JETSAM

Is rubbish that has been deliberately thrown into the water. It can originate from ships or it may be rubbish washed down from rivers that end up in the sea, it can even come from our holiday beaches.

I-SPY points: 10

Date:

PLASTIC CARRIER BAGS

Carrier bags are often used just once and then thrown away. When you use bags made of cotton or jute or even the heavy duty reusable plastic bags you are helping to save the planet from pollution.

I-SPY points: 5

Date: _____

WASTED WATER

Saving water should be one of our main concerns. Reducing the amount of water used when flushing the toilet, collecting used water to water plants and not keeping the tap running when cleaning your teeth are just some of the ways we can save water.

I-SPY points: 5

Date: _____

FAST FOOD REFUSE

The vast quantities of fast food refuse littering the streets of our towns and cities are a health hazard and attract vermin. Use a rubbish bin for the papers and containers and leftover food.

I-SPY points: 5

Date: _____

Index

First published by Michelin Maps and Guides 2010 ©
Michelin, Proprietaires-Editeurs 2010. Michelin and the
Michelin Man are registered Trademarks of Michelin.
Created and produced by Horizons Publishing Limited.
All rights reserved. No part of this publication may be
reproduced, copied or transmitted in any form without the
prior consent of the publisher. Print services by FingerPrint
International Book production – fingerprint@pandora.be.
The publisher gratefully acknowledges the contribution
of the I-Spy team: Camilla Lovell and Jordan Watts in the
production of this title.
The publisher gratefully acknowledges the contribution and
assistance of the following: Fairtrade, Ecover, Freecycle,
Love Food –Hate Waste, Soil Association, European ECO
Label, Bumblebee Conservation Trust, Keep Britain Tidy,
Woodland Trust, Blue Flag Beaches, People's Trust for
Endangered Species, Marine Stewardship Council, The
Wildlife Trust, Campaign for the Protection of Rural England,
Forest Stewardship Council, Royal Society for the Protection
of Birds, Steve Mountain at Oxford County Council. All logos,
images and designs are © the copyright holders and are
used with thanks and kind permission.
The publisher gratefully acknowledges the contribution of
Graeme Newton-Cox who wrote the text. The publisher also
gratefully acknowledges the co-operation and assistance
of the following who supplied pictures for this title: The
Camping and Caravan Club, Dominic Alves, Justin Perkins,
Michelin, Kamil Pachalko, unitaw, Cancer Research UK,
Ecover, David Fenwick, Mike Dent. Other images in the
public domain and used under a creative commons licence.

Answers: P6 Diesel Car, after its inventor, Rudolf Diesel (1858-1913). **P28** Lichens, two organisms that live together - a fungus and a very simple plant called an alga. **P56** Clean Buildings, Sulphur Dioxide.

I-SPY
One
Token
715146

HOW TO GET YOUR I-SPY CERTIFICATE AND BADGE

Every time you score 1000 points or more in an I-Spy book, you can apply for a certificate

Here's what to do, step by step:

Certificate

- Ask an adult to check your score
- Ask his or her permission to apply for a certificate
- Apply online to www.ispymichelin.com
- Enter your name and address and the completed title
- We will send you back via e mail your certificate for the title

Badge

- Each I-Spy title has a cut out (page corner) token at the back of the book
- Collect five tokens from different I-Spy titles
- Put Second Class Stamps on two strong envelopes
- Write your own address on one envelope and put a £1 coin inside it (for protection). Fold, but do not seal the envelope, and place it inside the second envelope
- Write the following address on the second envelope, seal it carefully and post to:

I-Spy Books
Michelin Maps and Guides
Hannay House
39 Clarendon Road
Watford
WD17 1JA